Love,
Jara

The ABCs of LOVE

This book
belongs to:

Lorelei

Presented by:
with much love,
Grammy

Leave a Mark for
love Nicole D
Camellen
♡+

The ABCs of LOVE

a love story

by **Susan R. Posterro**

Illustrations by **Jason Hughes** ❧ Edited By **Nicole Cannella**

The ABCs of Love: A Love Story
Copyright © 2016 Susan R. Posterro
All rights reserved.

Lampion Press, LLC
P. O. Box 932
Silverton, OR 97381

ISBN: 978-1-942614-20-3

Library of Congress Control Number: 2016945713

Formatting and layout by Amy Cole, JPL Design Solutions
Printed in the United States of America

2

To my mom, Emalynne~
Honoring your heart and
legacy will be my legacy.
I continue my promise to you of
planting seeds of
love from my heart;
understanding that and in faith,
they will grow when and
where they are intended to do so.

To my husband Kevin ~
Thank you for our love story.

3

Foreword

It starts with a spark.

A spark of inspiration bringing creativity to fruition.

A leading light that beckons a timeless tale.

As an author of two children's books, my personal flame was one sparked by compassion; to tell tales through a child's eyes to encourage empathy and caring through creativity.

The book you hold traces its spark back to a time of trials in the 1940s; to a letter written with profound love from a soldier father to his toddler daughter. It was a letter that lit a fire in that little girl's heart to carry love forward and be led by faith.

The daughter of a seamstress and a soldier, that little girl grew in faith and fortitude—determined to live as salt and light and to plant proverbial seeds of love.

That same light of faith coursing through the years and passing hands from that once toddler daughter all grown and caring for her own gracious girl.

And as a spark spreads to a flame, a faith fire was brought to fruition in the heart of the granddaughter of the seamstress and faithful soldier, who, though not a mother herself, longed to nurture that spark and cover others in its warmth.

Here grows the love story; one of two women's goals to be a part of God's grace and to wrap as many as could be touched in metaphorical and literal love.

Susan, the daughter of a missionary and granddaughter of that faith-filled soldier now waged her own war against anguish and sorrow in the form of blankets.

4

Sparks that led to seeds that led to the founding of an organization whose hopeful goal is to offer comfort through tangible touch and unsurpassed softness.

This book carries heartbeats of the past; of a soldier, a seamstress, a missionary, and a dreamer who wanted to do good.

Equally important, *The ABCs of Love* echoes the heartbeat of little fighters, soldiers in their own right, who have graced heaven's door and those who have survived to live on and spread their own sparks.

Each one, each letter, each seed, each alphabet angel, wrapped in the warmth from a spark that started over 70 years ago.

And it's still aglow.

How will you leave your mark?
What seeds will you plant?
Where will you find your spark ?

Seek it with faith and love and let God caress and bless the rest.

With Love,

–Nicole DeRosa Cannella
Author
Leaving a Mark
The Ribbit Exhibit

Once upon a time, there lived a little girl named Susie.
Susie was quiet and shy; with rose petal cheeks,
and dancing pig-tail hair.

Her favorite time of day was bedtime;
with its snuggles and stories.
One sleepy eve, her gentle mother tucked her in.
Susie felt snug-as-a-bug.

This night was just a bit different;
for Susie's mother gave her a gift.
As she tucked a special something into Susie's pajama pocket,
Susie asked her, "What are these?"

Her mother replied with light in her eyes...
"These are seeds; my daughter, dear...
Listen and hear.

They are seeds that only you can sow."
Her softly speaking mommy whispered to her:
"One day, you will go, go, go...

And sow each special seed with a loving deed.
No two seeds are the same sweet Susie.
Now remember to plant them all alongside you.

Each place you stop, each path you step,
everywhere you go, remember to leave
your seeds of love to grow."

Susie closed her eyes and drifted into seed-filled dreams.

9

A is for Acceptance

10

Alice is always accepting.

B is for Blessings

Bailey believes in blessings.

11

C is for Courage

Carter is clearly courageous.

D is for Doing good

Dorian does a world of good.

E is for Expressing gratitude

Emilio expresses great gratitude.

F is for Faith in forever

Frankie has forever faith.

15

G is for Gift-giving

Grayson gives gifts from his heart.

H is for **holding** on to Hope

Hunter holds on to hope.

I is for Inspiration

Isabella inspires others.

J is for Joy

Joe is so joyful.

K is for Kind-hearted

Katie-Anne has a kind, kind heart.

L is for Love

Lauren truly loves.

21

M is for Magical moments

Mac makes moments magical.

N is for Nurture

Nicholas nurtures hope.

23

O is for Open heart

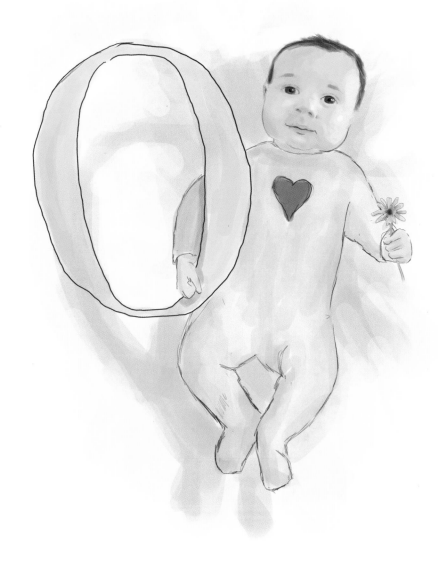

Oliver opens his heart to love.

P is for Peaceful

Parker is perfectly peaceful.

25

Q is for Quietly giving

Quinton quietly gives.

R is for Reciprocate

Raul reciprocates kindness.

S is for Sincerity

Sammy is sincere.

T is for Thoughtful

Tara is thoughtful through and through.

U is for Unwavering love

You can be a person of unwavering love.

V is for Values

Vito values his family.

W is for Warmth

Walter is warm-hearted.

X is for eXceptional

Xander is exceptional with his actions.

33

Y is for Yearn

Yasmine yearns for peace.

Z is for Zeal

Zach is zealous in being the best he can be...
and so too can you and I be.

Rubbing sleep from her eyes,
Susie's heart was filled with happiness.
She bounded from bed to tell of the many
new friends she remembered.

Wanting so to return for more time with her forever friends.
She wanted to go, go, go.

Each friend had taught her beautiful lessons of love.
Susie's mother wrapped her close and spoke...

"Sweet Susie, you're not really apart
...special friends will forever share a piece of your precious heart."

"But mommy," said Susie. "How will I know what happened to all of the special seeds of love?" Gently, her mother bent to kiss her daughter's head and said...

"When you plant seeds of love, each one will grow from a tiny seed into who and what it is meant to be.

You see, Susie...
When sown with love, more love
will grow and grow and...
on and on it will go."

As you close your eyes
tonight, hold your hands
close to your heart and
listen to it, and then write
the promise in your heart.
Tomorrow what seeds of
love will you plant?

39

Afterword

I will never forget the day in 2013 when my husband, Chris, and I walked our son, Sammy, into a lead-lined room, where every inch was wrapped in protective covering to prevent radiation exposure. The levels of radiation in that room would be so toxic that Chris and I were required to stay behind two 1,000-lb lead doors for five days, while Sammy stayed in that room, confined to the bed, alone. Sammy would be walking in there with nothing to protect or comfort him, but we knew this treatment could save his life.

In 2012, Sammy had been diagnosed with Stage IV High-Risk Neuroblastoma, a type of childhood cancer. Hearing the words "cancer" in relation to your 4-year-old baby is unimaginable. "Cancer? How is that possible?" I remember the night he was diagnosed reading about neuroblastoma and being sick to my stomach. These kids didn't survive! We were in shock and completely devastated. He had surgery immediately and then started intensive inpatient chemotherapy to try to lessen the disease that had spread throughout his little body.

A few months later we were told Sammy wasn't responding to treatment and we were hit with the reality of our situation like a ton of bricks. Childhood cancer is the #1 cause of death by disease in children, yet it receives only 4% of federal cancer research dollars and while pharmaceutical companies fund over 50% of adult cancer research, they fund very little for children.

Friends had already started a campaign to show support for our family while Sammy was in the hospital. They sold t-shirts and sent him pictures to make him smile when he was having rough days. They raised quite a bit

40

of money and we needed to decide what to do with it. A friend suggested we form a nonprofit foundation and make our own decisions about research projects to which we would like to donate.

At first we were hesitant, but then realized it gave us a source of hope. We might not be able to influence the treatment options available for Sammy, but we were determined that other families would not have to go through the same thing we did: the fear, uncertainty and desperation due to lack of new treatment or options.

In the summer of 2013 our journey brought us to Boston for a clinical trial. This trial was for MIBG Therapy, a high-dose radiation treatment available at only a handful of hospitals in the United States. It was difficult to conceptualize how our baby was going to do this alone for five days. He could not take anything into the room with him for comfort. Because of the radiation dose, anything that went in could not come out.

It was one night during this painful part of our journey that Binkeez for Comfort quietly came into our lives. One of the nurses brought me a package and said that it had been left at the nurses' station for Sammy. I opened it, knowing that he couldn't have it, but still curious. I knew right away what it was. Sammy was receiving a Binkeez for Comfort Blanket!

It was so soft, I couldn't help but snuggle it to my face. Throughout those days, I kept pulling it out to snuggle it.

Somehow, we made it through those days and I couldn't wait to give Sammy his new blanket! It was Dr. Seuss-themed and had a character holding an "I am Sam" sign on it.

Sammy loved it! We traveled home to Nebraska a few weeks later with our new Binkeez in tow.

It wasn't long before we started ordering Binkeez Blankets for the rest of our family. Sammy's Grandma ordered Binkeez as gifts for Christmas that year.

Meanwhile, Sammy's Superheroes Foundation had started making donations to research and while we felt good about accomplishing our mission, we were missing something and something important to us—the connection to families. As we began to identify this need, we thought about what brought Sammy and us comfort during the most difficult days—our Binkeez Blankets! We wanted every child with cancer to get a Binkeez Blanket from us! We decided that Sammy's Superheroes Foundation would fund all blankets sent to pediatric cancer patients across the country.

Over the last few years, this relationship both with our foundations and personally as friends has blossomed into one of the biggest blessings in my life. We are connecting with children and families on a personal, caring, and comforting level. Binkeez started giving back to our mission to fund childhood cancer research through online sales of their Binkeez for Comfort Blankets. The Give a Hug, Fund a Cure program at binkeezforcomfort.org provides 5% of monthly sales in donations to Sammy's Superheroes Foundation for childhood cancer research and plants seeds of love.

All of this arose from Susan's quiet-as-a-mouse blanket delivery to Sammy at Boston Children's Hospital.

-Erin Nahorny
Sammy's Mom

Susan R. Posterro

Susan is the Founder and Executive Director of Binkeez for Comfort. Binkeez for Comfort is a Guidestar Platinum-rated 501c3 nonprofit organization that supports sacred pediatric communities; those of babies and children struggling to survive life threatening illnesses, and acute developmental disorders.

Susan walked away from a lucrative 20-year career in law to carry forward the legacy and love of her mother Lynne, who has made over 40,000 blankets for children in developing countries.

Binkeez for Comfort Blankets are constructed from fabrics that are lead-free, hypo allergenic, and must withstand being independently tested to pass Consumer Safety Act Protection Laws and Government Safety Standards. Each Binkeez Blanket is hand-crafted as a conscious act of love with the intent to figuratively and literally wrap patients, and their families, with the power of unconditional love and hope of healing and survival. Binkeez for Comfort Blankets are made by hand and by heart.

This conscious act of love underlies the Binkeez for Comfort project that currently supports patients in the foremost children's hospitals in the United States. While Susan's intent was always to promote an experience of healing and survival through the Binkeez for Comfort project, hospitals are taking note of the clinical benefits of Binkeez to improve outcomes among patients and their families.

Emalynne McAtee

My father served in Europe in World War II and brought home an empathy for the children who were deprived as a result of war. That empathy transferred to my heart, but would not be shared until some time after his life ended from an abrupt and fatal heart attack, four weeks before his granddaughter Susan was born.

During my childhood, I watched Billy Graham on television and seeds were planted in my heart that would not bear fruit for many years.

When our children were grown, I finally discovered the personal love of our Savior that Billy Graham had spoken about. His son, Franklin Graham and fellow evangelist James Robison, conveyed the love and grace that God has for each of his children.

By 1999, when both my parents had entered heaven, it was finally possible to begin sharing the ripples of love that had been invested in my life; sharing the funds that had been left to me.

When September 11, 2001 devastated our collective heart, I knew something had to happen for good and wrote Samaritan's Purse asking if they would receive baby blankets like those hand made for our children. The letter came back with the assurance that Jesus always had time for children and the blankets would be welcomed.

Ethel Sinclair, a beautiful lady who was like a second mother to me and helped create the first blankets for our children, had no idea of her part in leaving a legacy of love.

My own mother's legacy of sewing and my father's heart for underprivileged children have been woven together in the ongoing journey of furnishing blankets to comfort children around the globe.

Our daughter Susan caught the vision and has carried forth Binkeez Blankets to comfort children fighting battles with serious illness. The legacy continues with her heart expressing gratitude for those who have invested in her life…and a legacy of love stitched into each blanket.

I believe my parents had no idea the legacy they would leave nor what God would be able to do with it.

-Lynne

Jason Hughes

Painting for over twenty years, artist and illustrator Jason Hughes aims to capture the soul of his subject in whatever medium he is working with. From portraiture to landscape, he strives to reveal the hidden truth of His nature lying just underneath the surface just waiting to be discovered.

The ABCs of Love is his first illustrated children's book. He currently is working outdoors painting *en plein air* and his work can be found at jasonhughesart.com.

Shades of pink and pale blue
Come from rainbows' precious hues;
And to many, in ribbon curled—
Those colors are symbols of
each boy and girl—
Who didn't see the sun of day—
But bathed in eternal light
Anyway...
For though they are gone—
Still , they are our friends...
These seeds are also sown for them.

—NDC

46

Acknowledgments

To all those of you who helped shaped this path of love and; from as young as I can remember even until today—each of you has blessed and wrapped my heart in your own beautiful and purposeful way.

> *As we express our gratitude,*
> *we must never forget that the highest*
> *appreciation is not to utter words,*
> *but to live by them.*
> –John F. Kennedy

To my illustrator Jason, with every letter that came into my mailbox and the tears of gratitude in forever documenting a soul and a journey through your heART, "thank you" will never be enough.

To my editor Nicole, there are no words to convey this journey together and my gratitude of your gift, of beyond an editor, in helping me honor my mother's heart, faith, and legacy and the root of Binkeez and what will always matter most—the bravest of lives.